MAYFLOWER
THE JOURNEY BEGINS
1620–2020

Anthology of Young People's Writing 2018

Edited by Nathalie Denzey

UPP
University of Plymouth Press

Paperback edition first published in the United Kingdom in 2018 by University of Plymouth Press, Roland Levinsky Building, Drake Circus, Plymouth, Devon, PL4 8AA, United Kingdom.

ISBN 978-1-84102-430-1

© University of Plymouth Press 2018
© Plymouth City Council 2018

A CIP catalogue record of this book is available from the British Library.

Editor: Nathalie Denzey
Publishing Assistants: Keziah Underhill, Abby Crawford and Mabel Khoo
Publisher: Paul Honeywill
Photographer: Alan Stewart
Cover artwork: *Visions of America*, Getty, Joe Sohm

Printed and bound by Short Run Press, Exeter

With contributions from University of Plymouth English with Publishing BA (Hons) Students, who ran workshops in the schools: Amy Potter, Hannah Govan, Abigail Joyce, Katie Collier, Laura Wortley, Laura Roberts, Natalie Redford

Foreword

Welcome to The Journey Begins, a creative writing collaboration between children from Plymouth, UK and Plymouth, USA to commemorate the sailing of the Mayflower in 1620.

These talented young writers have imagined what it is like to begin a journey, just as the ordinary families on the Mayflower began a journey 400 years ago. Together they take us through centuries of voyages with powerful stories and poems about the fear, adventure, sadness and excitement when taking those first intrepid steps.

Through their words, this anthology celebrates connections made since the journey of the Mayflower, considering what that voyage achieved and how it continues to resonate for both countries. Like all travellers, these children look, bravely, to the future while cherishing their past.

Charles Courtenay
Earl of Devon

This anthology is sponsored by the University of Plymouth and supported by Plymouth City Council.

Fireworks on the Hoe

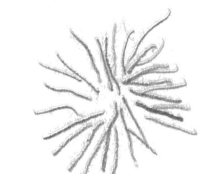

Fireworks
Loud, bright
Shining blazing booming
Exploding colourful bombs
Fire

Josephine Edwards
Age 9

Sky bombs
Bright, beautiful
Exploding, amazing, shining
Rockets shooting across the night sky

Theo Huxtable
Age 9

Artwork by Theo Huxtable

My Journey to the Hoe

The journey begins by getting into my mummy's car. I can still smell the popcorn from when we last went to the cinema. We drive past a river and see ducks splashing on the water. We park on the Hoe and I can smell the salt sea air.

I run about on the grass with my brother and I can feel the grass tickling my toes. I see the poppy wave and the sun shines on it, but the wind blows on my face and I start to feel cold.

My mummy buys me a lovely warm hot chocolate which warms my tummy, and we sit in the sun which warms my face as we watch the boats sail by on the sparkling sea. We go to the car and we drive home and do my homework and write my story.

The End.

Orla Joines
Age 7

Smeaton's Tower

Meets your eyes with the bursting colours
Eagerly you climb up scary ladders
All the stories it could tell, if only a voice
Tower of history and memories
On Plymouth's brilliant Hoe it stands
Nothing quite like it
Stairs made of concrete you climb to meet your destination.

Towering over your head
Outstanding journeys begin at the bottom
Waves splashing as it crashes over the tower in the wintery seasons
Eye opening views from the top
Red as a strawberry, as ripe as can be.

Evie Jones
Age 10

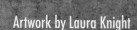

Artwork by Laura Knight

tanding proud on Plymouth Hoe
emories from long ago
very stormy winter's night
light at the top would shine nice and bright
o warn the ships near the Eddystone reef
f dangerous rocks that lie beneath
ow as the years went by it was time to go and
tand on a new base on Plymouth Hoe.

o tell the story of how it began
ut at sea with a lighthouse man
inding steps will take you back in time
veryone loves the steps they have to climb
eaching the top you can look out to the deep
blue sea and all across our lovely city.

Rosie Smale
Age 9

Artwork by Rosie Smale

Dartmoor – A Journey Begins

At Wistman's Wood on Dartmoor
The Devil starts his hunt at the spooky, dark wood at midnight.
His black, furry hounds have big red eyes and flaming nostrils.
They are looking for weary travellers on the moor.

Charley Bratt
Age 7

The Journey Begins

My Plymouth journey begins with Saltram.

A walking wonderland
Sprinkled with lush nature
An adventure that can never end
Filled with swaying pieces of bark and leaves
Perfect any season whatever the weather
A grey pathway with light green fur on either side
The rich, white mansion standing tall and proud
A journey you'll never forget.

Henry Shuttleworth
Age 10

The Journey Begins

My Plymouth journey begins with Plymbridge Woods.

The whistle through the trees
A loving bird song echoes all around
Families connected as the distance shortens
Cyclists zooming by
The water flow follows you down
Crunching beneath you, the leaves of autumn
Barking dogs prancing around the paths.

The beautiful brown soldiers standing in their green top hats
Dancing in the cool calm air
Butterflies brighten the woods
Animals of all shapes and sizes fly and scuttle around
As the journey finishes, wishing you could come back another day.

Isobel Rae Cameron
Age 10

The Journey Begins

Upon the moor, distressed, young Rosie, only nine,
Body shaking like a drum, a shiver cascaded down her
spine.

Her parents had forbidden her from the reserved woods.

Kayleigh Page
Age 9

The Journey Begins

We were halfway down the pier, thinking of what game to play first.

When the air raid started it was a Saturday in December. We were on the promenade pier on the Sound. All month the Germans have been attacking us, their bombs dropping like colossal boulders from the clear blue sky.

Eden
Age 10

My Plymouth Journey...

My Plymouth journey begins with the War Memorial.

Every soldier towers above us
Memories long and far
Of years of war and tragedy.

Ranks from Troops to Generals stand in this very place.
I come and I remember them.

A tsunami of poppies lies here and flurries of red swallow the site.

Loving families come here and I remember them well.

Elliot Jones
Age 10

Coming Home

My feet slap the pavement fast
The world blurs as I run
My world is so close
I inhale the faint smell of my fireplace
My dog yips with excitement
I yank open the chilled door handle
The carpet is fuzzy as I rip off my shoes
The wind stops howling when I slam the door
I breathe in the warm air
My bags fall to the floor with a clunk
I just let them stay there
I hug my dog close
I am home.

Celia Constantino
Age 13

Excited men cheering
Huge boats packing
Nervous people rowing
Upset families sobbing
The journey begins.

Sparkly oceans waiting
Little waves splashing
Worried men rowing
The journey begins.

Crashing waves and men asleep
Massive waves crashing
Big, dark thunder clouds
Sailors excited to go home
The journey is finished.

Samuel Harvey
Age 6

Artwork by Kayleigh Boxall

Armada Attacks

Prince Philip the second
at Queen Elizabeth he beckoned.
She turned down his advances
So what were their chances?

The Spanish launched their huge Armada
They wanted to see the English burn like lava.
When Sir Francis Drake was playing boules
He and his friends saw the Spanish souls.

His friends said, "We have to go and fight them off."
Drake replied, "We can finish our game, for them we will easily take off."
When the game came to an end
Drake said, "Let's go fight for our country and defend."

He went down to the Mayflower steps
And reached a boat in his depths.
He set alight some fireships and sent them towards the enemy.
That, he figured, would be the perfect remedy.

The Spanish saw the fireships were about to come.
All their bodies were going numb.
They shouted, "This is too dangerous, let's get out of here."
Drake gave out a mighty cheer.

They sailed back to Spain
Desperate and feeling the pain.
Drake laughed and shouted at them,
"Never come back again".

Jessica Davis and Poppy Laird
Age 11

Lost in the forest, nowhere to go.
Look at the stars, how beautiful they glow.
Then she remembered the warning from her kin.
For there lived Grace,
Deadly Grace.
For there lived Grace whose legend got under her
skin.

The road was a ribbon thrown away.
The moon was a bomb showing her prey.
Like the witch, the trees were grabbing,
And she was rushing –
Rushing – rushing –
She was rushing, so hard, that the pain was throbbing.

Squelch, squelch, squelch, SQUELCH, she waded
through the mud,
Rip, rip, rip, RIP, she cut herself, drew blood,
Running, dashing, racing, never looking back.
Her blood oozed –
Oozed – oozed – oozed –
Her blood oozed on the terrible track.

Suddenly, seeing success in her tired sight,
Finally the end of the morning light,
In front of the gate who was standing there?
But her swollen-faced father,
Her shell-shocked, distraught father,
"I've been worried sick. How do you DARE?"

Lily Anderson
Age 9

Wand

My inner poet
Is an English oak
Wand at
Olivanders.

I sit in a dark
Enclosed box
For weeks upon
weeks.

Laying and waiting
Waiting for my true
Master
A witch or wizard to
Guide me to my
Full potential.

Finally found by
Emily
A beautiful witch
That will guide me.

Chose her because
after all
The wand chooses
The witch.

Adam Blackington
Age 13

The Mayflower

It was a cold, dark and gloomy morning. The time had finally come for all of the 132 people to board the ship. Moods were flying high as the excitement bounced off the sides of the ship. It didn't take long for the passengers to realise that the journey wasn't quite going to be the experience they were hoping for.

Joe Massey

Artwork by Mya Staward

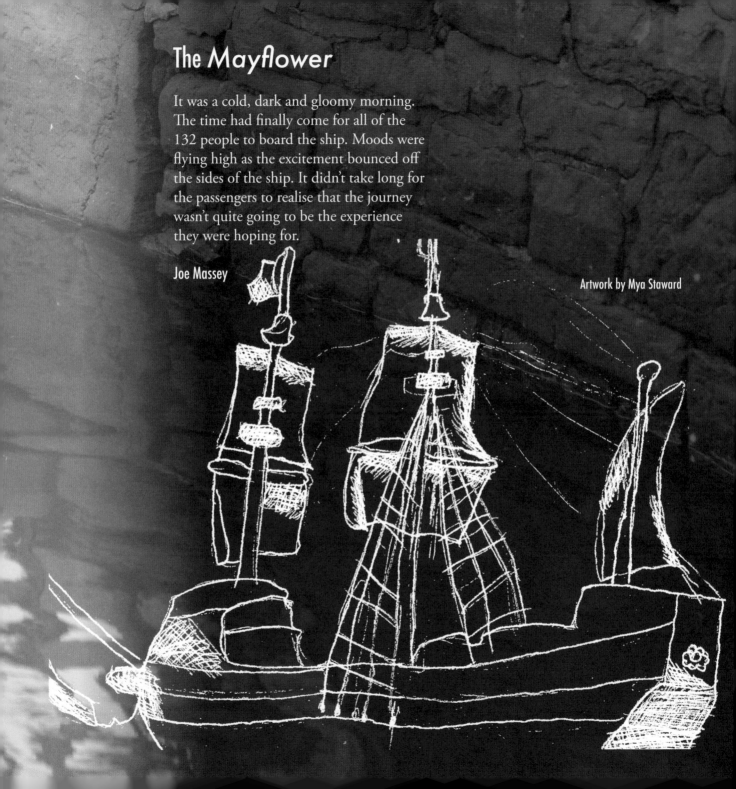

Tiny Raindrop

Tiny raindrop way up high, falling gently from the sky
Waving to the clouds, "Goodbye!"
Shooting through the sunlit blue as it gathers pace
Dazzling, sparkling colours all around, a rainbow full of grace
"Plop!" The raindrop lands on the rocky ground
Making such a beautiful sound
Soon he flows into the ice cold river
Tiny raindrop begins to shiver
At first the river is peaceful and calm
But soon it begins to do raindrop some harm.
Stormy currents make raindrop bounce and swirl
Dodging rocks in its path, always in a whirl
As the river greets the sea
Raindrop is happy. "At last I'm free!"
Watching the playful dolphins and the shimmering fish
Tiny raindrop has just one wish
The tide sweeps raindrop onto the soft, sandy shore
Where the warm sun pulls him into the sky once more
Up, up, up raindrop floats to see his friends. "Hooray!"
Today his long journey is over but tomorrow is a brand new
day!

Chloe Dickson
Age 8

The Pilgrims' Voyage

Sad, leaving my family
Curious, wondering what my future looks like.
Butterflies in my stomach
One single tear rolling down my cheek.
Putting my past behind me, and putting my
future in front.

Louie Flexen
Age 8

The New Land

I pushed through the crowd. Around me, dirty looks and yells reminded me why I was here, as each man punched me in the back every step I took. I veered closer to the small ship, where I shuffled silently up the slippery steps. The crowd stopped cheering abruptly.

"Good riddance," I heard as I began to quicken my pace, stepping awkwardly onto the small deck.

I had never meant to anger anyone, yet still everyone was angry at me. I had only meant to meet friends, not lose others. Yet somehow it had come to this. I noticed a familiar glance in the crowd as I looked down to see the next victim of the ship, and as I waved, she ignored me, disapproving, angry. Even those who had wanted me to be born wanted me dead. I watched as the mother I once loved died before me, as I turned my head, drifting towards the open ocean, empty and alone.

The weather became colder, windier and emptier as I travelled. The men around me became weak as I became stronger, each man missing home, yet I was at home. For I was no man, woman or child as each day became lonelier and only souls remained. I had become accustomed to this life, and as days became darker and emptier, each man had become a hopeless wreck, worried about not making it, yet I was still no man.

Sarah Small
Age 14

Dear Diary,

Today was probably the worst day we've had so far on the *Mayflower*. We are ever so thirsty and the crew never give us anything but beer and wine. The day started off as it always did, with people waking up next to rivers of foul liquid where chamber pots had spilt. When we wake up it is never day, or at least we never think it is. I really can't remember the last time I saw sunlight or stood up straight.

Lily Rainbow
Age 12

We've had a minor setback but still, other than that it's been fine. I never expected luxury. We spend most of our time on deck but at night it gets chilly so we go inside for warmth. But not comfort, especially now the *Speedwell* was deemed 'unfit' for travel. We had to return to land to get everyone aboard this ship, the *Mayflower*. I do have to say, with these extra people aboard it is pretty cramped in here! At night we're all stuck in a small room. It gets extremely warm and smelly in here and it's not what I signed up for!

Corey Richardson
Age 13

The Journey of the Mayflower

Pulling up to the shore, I felt great relief. I had been on that cramped ship for two whole months! There were some days when the weather was calm and I felt relaxed and other days when the weather was stormy and the sea crashed against the boat, nearly tipping the ship onto its side. During most of the storms I was hiding inside, too scared to go out on deck, which made everyone think me a bit foolish. As I clambered off the ship I felt happier than I'd ever felt before.

Ava Grace Gallagher
Age 10

Artwork by Ava Gallagher

The Piano (inspired by Aidan Gibbons)

While a tear was rolling down Fred's cheek, he was playing a sad, sombre tune. Soothingly, the tune reminded him of his wife.

Sorrow skidded through him. Suddenly, he felt another key being lightly tapped beside him. Magically appearing, the ghostly figure kissed him on the cheek. Slowly his wife disappeared.

Suddenly another memory ran through his mind. Breathing heavily, the man ran through the battlefield with his brother. They weren't expecting anyone to die today. Panting heavily, his brother was shooting their enemies. But all of a sudden Fred's brother was dead. As he held the lifeless body, a stream of guilt ran through him. He let his brother die.

Whispering quietly, Fred's grandson opened the present that had been passed down generation to generation. The present was a hobby-horse. More and more memories raced to his mind, the exciting memories of when he was riding the hobby-horse. But he was happy that it was being treated carefully.

The boy whizzed up and down majestically like the wind. He had never had this much fun in his life! The boy came back to sit next to his grandfather to play the piano. The tune came to an end and the grandson played the last note of the tune.

Mara Coman
Age 9

The Mayflower

I was docking the boat with my people, and we were making sure we were all set on the *Speedwell* before we left. The boat's sails shot up and and spread its wings, and we were off. The gloomy water splashed up the boat while the crew were arguing, but I didn't know why they were acting so enraged.

Suddenly everyone was rushing up to the deck and they were shouting very loudly. I got an idea of what was being shouted: "There's a leak, help us." I didn't know what to do as everyone wasn't being calm at all so I had to improvise. I stood up with courage in my head, I took a deep deep breath and, "Everyone stop, turn this boat around and we can repair at Plymouth."

Deon Darby

Darkness

Creeping in to fight the light for its place
As quiet as a black cat creeping from an alley
Slowly chewing at the light each day
The iniquity of the darkness using everyone's sins to become more powerful
Scaring kids before bed
The eternal dance with the Moon and Sun
pauses each night
only to return
Immortal.

Eric Godlewski
Grade 5

Stones

Seven shining silver star stones
Encircling a small girl
She walks freely
Light on her feet

Square stones sailing silently
At the girl
She doesn't see them coming
Oblivious

Seemingly she's safe
Then she's hit
Pelted with the force
Of an army

Six square stones scuffling
With shining stars
One destroyed
Six more to go

Star stones sadly suffer
Taken out
With brute force
A hopeless fight

She stands still
Solemn
Staring at the rubble
Tears streaming down

Square stones surrounding
A pale girl
As she picks up
Shattered pieces

Star stones stuck sloppily
Back together
The girl tries
With little luck

She stands shakily
Surrounded by
A sloppy star stone
No longer bright

Stepping shyly
Back into the world
Grasping at the star
She carries on.

Ava Rose
Age 15

Ship, ship, ship
Going on a trip
One, two, three
Sailing on the sea

Big, medium, small
One is very tall
Where will they go?
Does anybody know?

Mickey Smith
Age 8

Pen

A pen dreams about
Gracefully dancing over paper like a ballerina
With the ability to ruin lives, bring tears to eyes, and bring
laughter into the air

A pen thinks about
The impact it has on a young girl in need of an escape
And the way she's heartbroken when it finally runs out of ink

A pen remembers
The words it's written, the cries out for help that were hidden
away in its writing
The beautiful writing that won't see the light of day

A pen forgets
The number of pockets it's seen and the hands it's been placed in
Some warm and eager to write but some cold and distant

A pen tells us
A life story, a poem, maybe even a tragedy
A pen can tell us anything.

Zoe Jean Gilmore
Age 13

Forgotten Lyrics

Battered and bruised the journey began
Muffled voices covered muffled screams
People packed a dime a dozen
The cold bit on your fingers
The water corroded your skin.

Jay Confue and Becca Harvey
Age 15

Huge boat floating
Nervous crew going
Scared men crying
Empty seas waiting
The journey begins.

Smooth seas splashing
Poorly people sitting
cheerful people eating
This journey is great.

Sick people tumbling
Upset people rolling
Sick people dying
When will this journey end?

Poorly people groaning
Land is spotted
The journey has ended at last.

Finbar Stevens
Age 6

September 10th, 1620

Dear Diary

Today on the *Mayflower* was not a good one. The waves were monstrous as the wind wildly whipped the sails. Fear was trapped on everybody's faces while we were thrown this way and that upon the water-soaked deck. Crash! shouted the waves, as they lapped against the side of the boat, almost toppling people over.

Annabelle Everritt
Age 12

My Plymouth Journey begins with Charles Church

A church that stands lonely
It watches the cars go by and round
Round, Round, Round in circles
Like a merry – go – round.

It has seen many things
Bombs, planes, guns and soldiers
Allies to enemies
The stories it could tell, if only a voice.

A church that stands lonely
Once people would sing hymns
Now only the ghosts of the Vicar, the people, the children
They haunt the church, still whispering their prayers
Singers happy hoping the war would end.

Elena Price
Age 10

The Journey

The crackling woke me up, sweet smells of the roast boar
as it scorched on the fire.
Then a speck of dust of the blanket of sea.
Nothing to admire yet. As the speck became a smudge we
gathered and watched the ink travel across the fabric of time
and take the form of a boat.

And as it approached, steps from the softest feet imprinted
on our soil.
As the black tears of a murderer fell to our ground, I realised
that the ink had tainted us.
The pure sky now dark with clouds, the bright fire flickering
out in the empty moonlight.

The scarlet bottle of our blood all spilled on the sand, the
quill is a sword - the paper your hand.

Saahithya Aroori
Age 14

The Mayflower

There were a lot of people on the ship and that made me feel claustrophobic. I was sick over the side of the *Mayflower*. I heard the Captain say that there might be one hundred and thirty-two people on the ship. The cook was cooking the fish we caught and yelled, "Dinner's ready!" We sat down and ate the fish. The taste was tasty and delicious.

A week later I saw the new born baby squealing. I really wanted to see land but I couldn't see any. It was a calm day with a bit of breeze. The crew and I were singing sea shanties merrily.

Two months later my Captain saw some seagulls and shouted, "Land Ahoy!" I was really happy to see land. As we saw land, we anchored in America and jumped down on the fresh, sandy beach.

Maisy Edmonds
Age 9

Extract
Day 10:

I despise this boat. Also I'm sorry I haven't wrote in here for a number of days. I haven't been doing anything except eating,sleeping and using the toilet. Me and John have been trying to keep each other entertained but it is very easy to get bored on this boat.

Day 61:

We have finally arrived and it was great. We got off the boat in this amazing new land. We started to look around but we soon started to realise that there were other people on the land. We thought they were going to attack us but they didn't. Instead they helped us get food and water.

Edie Spooner

Freedom

Wind rushes
Through Wings.
High above

Everyone.

Leave any
Troubles
   Worries
      Pain
       Everything
Behind.
   Ground-bound.
Fly free.

Sam Bisson
Age 14

Artwork by Maisy Edmonds

The Mayflower Journey

The monster that was to set sail tomorrow towered above the dock and rocked precariously from side to side. The sea chucked and rolled in dangerously high waves that roared at the awaiting voyagers. The decks were washing out and the gangway was posed in an upright position, straining on its holdings. Thousands of people bustled in crowds of varying sizes without order or conformity. Evidently there was a storm brewing, and it was going to be a rough night for the people looking up at the ship in anticipation. The gangway gave way and landed with a slight bounce on the dock. Time for the voyage of the generation.

Lauren Venn
Age 16

Going Back in History
My Plymouth Journey begins with Charles Church

On a roundabout it lies
Like an island surrounded by rocky seas
Children stare out of car windows in wonder
A picturesque scene of history
I wish I knew how it survived
A wounded soldier never giving up
Showers of bombs fell on it
It stands strong like a giant
A landmark of Plymouth never to be forgotten.

Georgia Stiles
Age 10

White

White is mellow, soft, sweet
Like a winter sleigh ride, or vanilla ice cream.
White is the sound of the soft sand, crunching beneath my feet
Or the white cotton ball clouds, floating along at the beach.
White is laughter, smiles, fun
Like the white dandelion fuzz, flying in the summer sun.
White is my shoelaces as I fly across the track
Or the white shoe holders on the snowboard
That close with a snap, and a clack.
White is the light of the morning sun
Or the moon in the night, saying you've had enough fun.
White is my Converse as I prance down the hall with my two best Friends.
White is the page your continuous story is on, it never ends.
White is the grips for bars, that cover my blisters
And white is the car I drove home in with my new baby sister.
White is the color of a head full of thoughts
Or my white shirt that has a stain, from spilling my applesauce.
White is the team jacket I wear to my meets.
White is the color red, or green, or pink try to beat.
White.

Ella Hall
Age 11

Home Park

Green, white
Shouting, running, scoring
Fans cheering their local team
Stadium

Roman Gabor
Age 9

I am...

I am an artist's loft, covered with color, and splattered with enlightenment

I wonder how I will make the next person in my life happy
I hear cheerful laughter from the other joyful ones around me
I see other pieces of art, each one telling its own story
I want to love everyone, and I want everyone to love me

I am an artist's loft, covered with color, and splattered with enlightenment

I pretend that each streak of paint is another chapter to life's beautiful tale
I feel the kindness of others filling my heart
I touch the world, one soul at a time
I worry if I'll make any mistakes in the process
I cry when others do the same

I am an artist's loft, covered with color, and splattered with enlightenment

I understand that everyone should have peace and love in their life
I say that I'll be loving and loyal
I dream that everyone will count on me when times get rough
I try to make everyone feel good about themselves
I hope that I help people discover who they really are

I am an artist's loft, covered with color, and splattered with enlightenment.

Nick D'Ortona
Age 13

The tears ran down her delicate face. Her heart, as pure as gold, sank to her feet, her long pink nightgown flapping in the Autumn wind.

She just wanted to run inside and to find her mother and father. Her little brother Charles was pulling numerous of her little pink ribbons out. Her long blond curls were flapping in the wind. The dreaded officer slowly stumbled over to them.

"No sign my dear children, God bless them if they are alive." Officer Physico put his arm around them. The blazing fire's reflection was in her tearful grey eyes.

Freyja Trim
Age 11

George and I were learning about the Book of Kings when it all began. At St Andrew's Church, Sunday School was always a bit boring as it was only me and my brother. The Luftwaffe hovered over the city, drowning it in explosions. Unsurprisingly, this had been going on for a while in Plymouth, as it's a big naval city.

Only a few months ago, life had been different. Dad had been with us, Mum hadn't been worried and and we hadn't been in danger of being bombed. Before the war family life had been much better. We could go on daytrips. The city had been a gleaming landmark of excitement and the school had been much better.

As the air raid siren wailed, my dreams drifted away and reality came back to me, fear gripped me. As all the other children were being led out my stomach was in knots. The air raid warden was yelling now; "Bomb incoming! Quick to the air raid shelter!"

Sean Davy
Age 10

On the *Mayflower* I could see the waves crashing on the ship. I could smell the sick of those who got ill. Some days it was freezing when others were so hot, it felt like the air was on fire. I could hear the children screaming as the lightning flashed. The babies crying as the thunder crashed.

I could hear the dogs barking. I could taste the beans for dinner. I could see the rats and mice as the dogs chased them. The storms were fearsome and one man fell in the water but the man luckily grabbed a rope and was saved. I could smell the fishy air of the ocean.

Holly Melmoth
Age 8

The Pilgrimage Poem

Hope shone brightly in the distance
The ocean between us
A risk to our existence.
Our journey constantly grows in length
Yet our crew's faith
Keeps our strength.
Our aim is to spread more life
Uncovering a whole new world
Where we can live without strife.
From Plymouth we set sail
Expectations are high.
"All Aboard!" I call out
As we pilgrims pray to the sky.
So join us once more on our trip
As we unite aboard our ship.
We will learn forever more
The story of the *Mayflower*
And how it washed ashore!

Katie Paterson, Helen Seymour, Maddie Clark, Alex Lamerton
Age 14

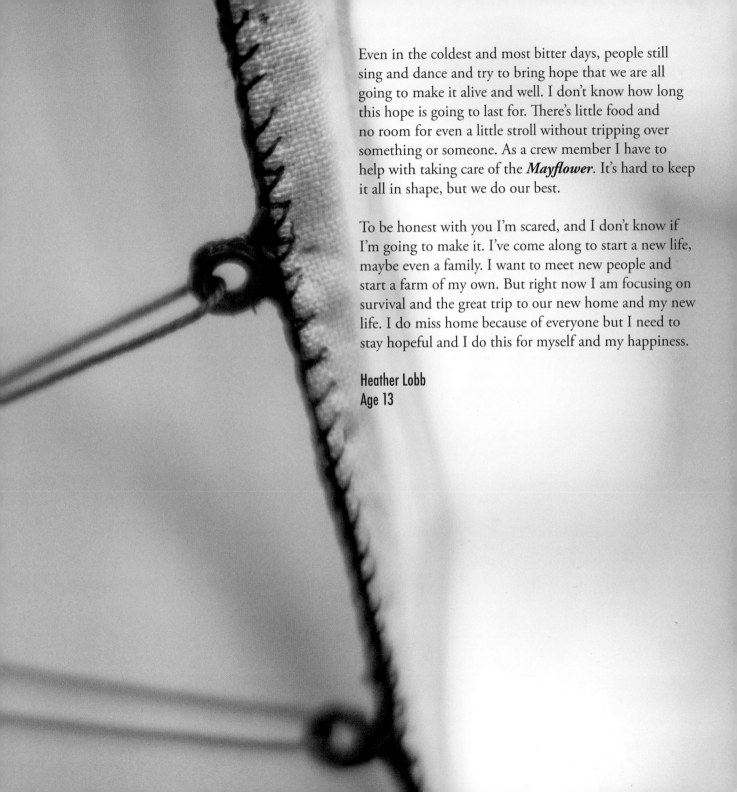

Even in the coldest and most bitter days, people still sing and dance and try to bring hope that we are all going to make it alive and well. I don't know how long this hope is going to last for. There's little food and no room for even a little stroll without tripping over something or someone. As a crew member I have to help with taking care of the *Mayflower*. It's hard to keep it all in shape, but we do our best.

To be honest with you I'm scared, and I don't know if I'm going to make it. I've come along to start a new life, maybe even a family. I want to meet new people and start a farm of my own. But right now I am focusing on survival and the great trip to our new home and my new life. I do miss home because of everyone but I need to stay hopeful and I do this for myself and my happiness.

Heather Lobb
Age 13

The Legend of King Arthur
A Play

Scene 1

St. Paul's Cathedral, London, Anglo-Saxon times.

Narrator: Long ago, when forests were still enchanted, a warrior king named Uther Pendragon ruled Britain. When Uther died many imposters tried to claim the throne, including the dead king's step-daughter Morgan le Fay.

Knight 1: *(Grandly)* King Uther Pendragon is dead! We need a new monarch! Who shall it be?

Morgan le Fay: (excitedly, rushing forward) Ah yes, the king is dead! Long live me, the queen. I shall be marvellous!

Merlin: *(Chuckling, hands on hips, throwing his head back)* You're a witch, Morgan. You'll never be queen!

Knight 2: Who will be our ruler? *(Majestically, pointing to himself)* I would make a great king!

Knight 3: *(Speaking even louder)* Surely I, the bravest knight of all, should be the next king!

(They continue to bicker as they walk into the Christmas service).

Narrator: Merlin the magician decided to use his powers to ensure that Uther's true heir gained the kingdom. During the Christmas service, Merlin magicked a great stone with a sword set in it.

Merlin: *(Closing his eyes and waving his arms mysteriously)* From a little pebble, a mighty sword and stone will grow!

(Merlin disappears. Some knights ride past and see the stone)

Knight: *(Jumps off his horse and walks over to the stone)* What's all this then? Why on earth is there a sword protruding from this rock?

Knight 1: *(Pointing to the writing in front of the stone)* Ooh, Look here! There's an

This archway is called a tympanum. From here, you can see a square concrete doorway. This comes from a 17th-century hospital that was actually a Workhouse, called the Hospital of Poor's Portion. It was thought, in those days, that hard work was a good cure for illnesses.
Elizabethan Gardens, New Street.

Knight 3: *(Loudly)* Whoso pulleth out this sword of this stone is the right wise king born of all England.

(Pulling with all his might, he tries to pull it out) I think it's stuck!

Narrator: After the service, all the knights and nobles tried to remove the sword, but none succeeded.

(A queue of noblemen develops and they take turns to try)

Bishop: *(Impatiently stepping forward)* Well, it's obvious that the king isn't anyone here! We'll hold a jousting tournament to find him. *(Urgently)* Messengers! *(Three messengers come running)* Spread the word across the land, so that everyone knows.
Messengers: *(Bowing)* Yes sir.

Ghalyah, Luke, Zac, Joshua & Lola
Age 7

Trapped inside Buckland Abbey!

I'm in Buckland Abbey but it's locked. I'm trapped! Some people would say it would be really cool, but to be honest it isn't. I was walking around with my group until the guide said we could walk around on our own but not to go far. But I wanted to explore more. I didn't realise the time and it was time to go and I got left behind, and I was kind of excited because it meant I could explore places where we didn't go. But now I'm frightened. I don't know if I'm going to get out.

James Mintoft
Age 10

Sophie and the Tudor Experience

Sophie, her mum and dad and her little Pomeranian Boo! were going for a walk down by the Hoe.
"Can we stop by the Tudor Gardens?" said Sophie pleadingly.
"Yes, I don't see why not!" replied her mum cheerily.
"Yes!" cheered Sophie excitedly.

Sophie had been learning all about the Tudors at School. She had taken a great interest in this subject and enjoyed admiring all the fancy costumes and wacky and funny foods.

"Yey," said Sophie. "We're here!"
Sophie looked around. Flowers were blooming everywhere and white and red poppies were blossoming before their very eyes. Red, white, pink and yellow. There were flowers everywhere.
"Look, I found a Tudor rose…" began Sophie.

WHOOOOOSHHH...

"WHAT JUST HAPPENED!" shrieked Sophie.
Sophie was in a round object and was falling forwards!
Wait, she was in a massive clock. Years, eras and dates
whizzed past her like zooming rockets on firework day!

Sophie managed to catch one of the little slips. It had
"Stone Age" written on it. Sophie had a look at the
paper, wait, it wasn't paper. It was a thin piece of bark!
Sophie threw it back and it flew away like a bird!

Suddenly Sophie stopped falling. A piece of paper had
fallen lightly into her arms. It read,

"Your destination is reached. The TUDOR Era!"

Anvi Purayir
Age 10

What an Amazing Journey...

My Plymouth journey begins with Buckland
Abbey.

The drums of time have rolled and ceased.
The antiquated building still captivates me.
I could barely comprehend something so old, so
enduring.

How could something stretch over time and still
be for my eyes to behold?
Here are the hallways where the famous sailor,
who circumnavigated the globe,
Must have ambled.

The beauty of the picturesque landscape was
mesmerising, including the orchards and the
brambles.

Standing, gazing at the historic artifacts.
An ocean of vibrant colours swallowing the dusty
house.

For a second, I'm back in the past,
With the ghosts of families having a midnight
feast.

What a journey.

Akshita Rajguru
Age 10

Back of replica chair from the Tudor period. This chair is
part of the Mayflower Museum collection.

Where There Is War

Where there is war, there is war in thee
There is no cure or quarantine
It's a disease without an antidote
With rivers of blood where bodies float
Bullets flying
People dying
Children crying
It's a road in which no one survives
As armies fall and others rise
Bombshells blowing
Soldiers killing
Barrels smoking
Blood spilling
Where there is war in thee, there is war in I
And this world is running out of time.

Ronald Tilton
Age 14

Pewter Plate
From 1300 to 1800, pewter was as familiar as our pottery dishes are today.

The Pilgrims knew there would be trees in America, so they could make things from wood, but they didn't know what else there was. They had to pack everything they thought they might need onto the *Mayflower*.

Kenzie's Journey

She'd an old, tattered hat on her long, golden hair
With tears dripping down her raw face.
A bright, fleecy coat that was broken, torn and ripped from
the chase
Her boots were wet and dirty, letting in water and damp.
Kenzie raced to escape from Dartmoor.
The derelict house on Dartmoor
Fleeing the old, crazy woman on Dartmoor
As the moon shone as bright as a lamp.

The wind was an angry ghost circling her round and round
The moon was a face of a skull and Kenzie fell to the ground
The road was a venomous tarantula hung from a shed.
And Kenzie was alone screaming –
Screaming – screaming
Kenzie was alone screaming, longing to be in her bed.

Crunch – crunch, crunch – crunch
Went the mysterious man hunting his prey.
Aaah – aaah; Aaah – aaah, raced
The screaming girl through the sticky clay
Over the wobbly bridge through the cold, gloomy night.
Kenzie was racing – racing – racing
Kenzie was dreaming for the morning light.

And all of a sudden to her relief, her home was in sight
She twisted and turned fast on her feet following the moonlight
Fast and furious over the old bridge and who should be waiting scared
But Kenzie's old, shaken mother.
Kenzie's rejoicing and relieved mother.
"You've been to the house the old, derelict house?
You must never ever venture there."

Maddison Davies-Hext
Age 9

The Journey Begins...

In the cold, frosty winter of 1972 a local Plymouth tailor named Stuart Turner was angrily making his way to the artist Robert Lenkiewicz's gallery to discuss all the homeless, alcoholic criminals that were staying at the gallery. Robert told him that homeless people are still people, but they have just had some bad luck in the past. Stuart didn't agree and wanted them gone.

Robert stormed out of the room leaving Stuart all alone. Feeling mad, Stuart picked up one of Robert's paintings of a homeless man sitting miserably in the freezing rain. He held it above his head, about to smash it, when he looked up into the homeless man's eyes and in a flash he found himself outside in the pouring rain, wearing a ripped suit.

As Stuart wandered around, trying to find shelter, people walked into him, pushing and shoving him out of the way. He felt like he was invisible. He strolled for ages until he came to a dark, gloomy subway and decided to sit there and think about what had happened. It began to get dark as the wind whistled through the subway tunnels.

As Stuart tried to get to sleep he saw a dark, shadowy figure approaching. It came closer and closer until it said, "Hello! My name's Mark. Would you like some company?"

"If you like, but I'm not very good company," Stuart said sadly.
"It's ok, everyone needs a friend," Mark replied.

The two men sat in silence until Stuart began to shiver with his teeth chattering loudly.

"Here you go," Mark said softly. As he gave Stuart his brown, dirty blanket Stuart carefully took the scruffy blanket from Mark and, even though it smelled, and he would never normally touch it, he wrapped it round himself as if his life depended on it.

The next day Stuart woke up and Mark was gone, but his dirty blanket was still wrapped around his shoulders. Then Stuart realised that even though Mark had nothing he still gave away what he did have. At that moment his tummy started to rumble and he remembered how hungry he was. He reached into his pockets, hoping to find some money, but they were empty.

He wandered around the Barbican looking through bins for food. He found some old chips and ate them as fast as he could, despite them being cold and covered in dirt. He looked up and saw a giant mural on the wall of Robert Lenkiewicz's gallery. It was the first time he had really looked at a piece of Robert's work and he realised what a talented artist he was. Standing there, in the freezing December sunshine, staring up at the painting, he found himself back in the gallery, holding the painting of the homeless man above his head. He slowly lowered it and recognised the man staring back at him. It was Mark!

As Stuart gently placed the painting back on the easel Robert returned and Stuart said, "I'm so sorry. I want to help you, and I don't want the homeless people to go."

"That's very nice of you. What made you change your mind?" Robert asked.

"Someone made me realise that homeless people are humans too and we should all just be kind to each other."

The next day Stuart threw a party for Robert, inviting all the local press, to unveil the mural and to celebrate Robert's talent.

Jessica Vanner
Age 10

We were finally at our destination, two whole months we had sailed, and I felt so relieved to be on land. It was very cold but that wasn't new since I had witnessed many storms with winds as cold as ice on my travels. I was so excited to be off that old wooden boat – and so were my friends – that we all forgot about the mourning and despair of our fellow sailors, and as a snowflake melted on my nose, I began to miss the other sailors too. Suddenly, as my stomach churned like a raging storm, I began to wonder how we were going to grow crops. After all, the food on the ship tasted horrid. The meat tasted like rubber, the apples were not succulent and the bread was soggy. I couldn't feel my feet. It was as if they had disappeared in my wet soggy socks and my back ached because the beds felt like rocks. We all had different jobs (they were really hard). We had to do things like scrub the deck or hoisting the flags. I think I swallowed a tooth after slipping on the wet soapy floor and landing on my face.

Mya Staward
Age 10

Drake the Protector

I was cold, wet, tired. It was dark. I was scared. I was alone…
at least I thought I was. Trapped in Buckland Abbey, not
knowing what to do, where to go, what if I never got out?
What if there was a noise, a great big noise? I was scared a
massive monster was going to come and gobble me up – but it
was just the wind, I was imagining things!

Charlotte Rose Young
Age 10

Horn book (replica)

A school book originating from the fifteenth century. A sheet containing the
letters of the alphabet and a prayer was mounted onto a wooden frame with
a handle, that could then be tied to a belt. A transparent layer of horn was
tacked over the top to stop the writing from getting damaged.

On display in the Mayflower Museum.

Ocean City

Waves crashing on the shore
Plymouth's oceans are not a bore.
People litter and take it for granted
That's why the beauty never lasted.
Children run to splash and play
But parents often drag them away
For they don't know the power of the sea
And just how powerful it can be.

It's full of animals big and small
And high cliffs where rocks fall
So this place cannot be gritty
For this is Britain's Ocean City.

People come from all around
Just to hear the sound
Of waves crashing on the rocks.

Jessica Baker
Age 9

Prologue (35 years before)

Darni Greyhold sat at the edge of his bed and sighed with great tiredness. He'd had a long life and now he wanted to pass on his family tradition. He told his butler to get his granddaughter. Serena Jones came running up the stairs to his bed instantly.

"You must pass the family tradition on to Christopher. Once he has found this special place in our dreams he must go by family tradition and call it Ameri-"…

Suddenly Darni inhaled sharply, but it wasn't enough. His last word came out as "gara", then his eyes closed and his spirit rose up to heaven above.

Fiacre Chong
Age 9

ISLAND HOUSE

REPUTED TO BE ONE OF THE HOUSES
WHERE A GROUP OF ENGLISH PURITANS,
SINCE KNOWN AS THE PILGRIM FATHERS,
WERE ENTERTAINED ASHORE PRIOR TO
THEIR FINAL DEPARTURE FOR AMERICA
ON THE 6TH SEPTEMBER 1620
IN THE 'MAYFLOWER'.

CITY OF PLYMOUTH 1976

Believed to be built
in 1572, Island House
is a jettied building,
meaning that the upper floor
projects beyond the floor below.
This gives more space in the house,
without obstructing the street. You can
this House on the Barbican, not far from
the Mayflower Steps.

As the perishing breeze brushed my face I stepped foot onto the sandy shore. I thought of the two months on the small, drab *Mayflower*. All the hustle and bustle, no fresh food and we didn't have a wash! This whole place felt and looked incredible. The luscious nature shone at me like the sun as I came closer to the unexpected snowy place. As the rest of the crew came to the shore, I was confused as my warm breath misted the cold air around me. The ferocious wind could have blew me off my feet as I tried to find shelter for everyone on the ship.

A couple of minutes later, I saw someone I believed to be a Native American. Other crew members had journeyed to these shores before and have told tales of these people.

Xander James Cave
Age 11

The *Mayflower* Journey

Dear Aunt Mary
We have arrived in the New World, but now I am beginning to think we should never have left home. I know Father had had a hard time in England for worshipping at the Separatist church but I do wonder if it was as hard as this. We arrived in the freezing cold, bitter, bitter wind and I'm sure the snow is imminent.

Finley Martin
Age 13

This plaque is on the Island House on the Barbican. It lists the passengers who set sail on the *Mayflower*.

CHRISTOPHER MARTIN

His wife
SALAMON PROWER

WILLIAM MULLINES
His wife
JOSEPH his son
PRISCILLA his daughter
ROBERT CARTER his servant

WILLIAM WHITE, wool carder
SUSANA his wife
RESOLVED and PEREGRIENE (born on
WILLIAM HOLBECK and EDWARD TH

STEVEN HOPKINS of Wotton-under-Ec
ELIZABETH his wife
GILES and OCEANUS (born on this voy
CONSTANTA and DAMARIS his dau
EDWARD DOTY and EDW

Travelling Across Seas

I can still remember the day we set off. The boat was large and the masts were high up in the air, towering over us. Day after day, all around us, was only ocean. Lots of people around me were resting or sleeping on the floor. Only a couple of people were eating or playing a game.

About a month in, everyone was feeling quite nervous but excited to get to America. We were scared, because so far we had really unpleasant weather conditions. By now, everyone started to smell dreadful from not having a wash in ages. That really bothered me because I would have to stick with it for the rest of the time on the boat. Every windy day, the salty smell was overwhelming and sometimes unbearable. Every day, every hour people were moaning and groaning about how much space they have. That very same week, late at night, everyone was woken up to the sound of a baby crying and we all knew it was our fellow passenger, who gave birth to a beautiful baby girl. In the morning, when we woke up, everyone was talking about the baby. That changed everything because people had to be a lot quieter so they didn't wake the baby.

When people started to get annoyed about being on the boat for ages, the others would just tell them why we left Plymouth in the first place, and that was so we could get away from everything, so we could go over and start a new life in America, to start afresh.

Until one day, after what felt like a whole year, we could finally see land.

"Hooray!" we all cheered. After a while the Captain stopped sailing the *Mayflower*. The crew then lowered the boats into the ocean, so they could carefully take the people over to land. I was lucky enough to get onto the first boat. As the men were rowing, as the land slowly neared, it seemed to bring new life into everyone so they rowed faster and faster.

As we got even closer to land everyone's excitement came bursting out. While we were talking on the boat, we seemed to realise no one cared any more if the food was rotten, or if we were cold. We just wanted to get to land.

Kayleigh Boxall
Age 11

Autumn in a Glance

When Autumn comes peeping round the corner
Summer is over.
We will be sitting round the fire
And we will have blankets for a cover.

Fireworks will bang
And the fire will blaze
It will be a great time
Except for the morning haze.

We will be kept happy
Leaves will crunch.
We will jump
And cows will munch.

Crash! The fireworks shoot up
Fawkes and the gunpowder plot.
Extreme colours and light
And the fire will get red hot.

Rebekah Lavers
Age 11

Butterfly

Pretty on one side
Same on the other
Gentle as the wind that blows through my hair
Soft as the pillow I rest on
Beautiful as the stars that come out every night
Flies smooth as silk
Gliding through the air
Silent as sleeping children resting in their beds.

Madalyn Harris
Age 8

On the Hoe...

My Plymouth Journey begins with Smeaton's Tower.
Smeaton's Tower stands tall and proud, overlooking Plymouth
Sound.

It's bold in colours, Red and White.
It stands on Plymouth Hoe, what an amazing sight!

At first it was isolated out at sea
But now it stands for the whole of Plymouth to see.

You can climb to the top, oh what a view!
There's Drake's Island, Jennycliff and the Lido too.

And yet this tall, towering candy cane still stands today
Making memories with us. Hooray! Hooray!

Lucy Harris
Age 10

My Mum's Graduation

My half term was marvellous because I went to my mum's graduation. It was at the Guildhall. My mum was superb! She had to wear a really weird, square, black hat for the graduation. She wore a very pretty, silver dress. Over the top she had a gown that was sweeping on the floor like a long dress. It was like a cloak! It was black on the outside and inside it was dark red. I saw my mum shake hands with a man on the stage. At the Guildhall we had a tremendous picture taken by my grandpa. He did a really good job.

I knew it was a really special day for my mum because before the graduation, she had worked so hard. After watching my mum at the Guildhall, we went to the Slug and Lettuce for lunch. I had a yummy burger with amazing, delicious chips and scrumptious onion rings. Then we took a photo of the whole family. When I saw the picture I was flabbergasted. We all looked amazing! My mum's face was so happy. After that, we went to get my mum's photo put in a frame. When we went into town I went on the big wheel for a treat. It really was colossal!

I was so excited that day and I was so proud of my mum.

Cece Edwards
Age 7

Artwork by Cece Edwards

The Journey Begins

My Plymouth journey begins with Smeaton's Tower.
A tall red and white striped modern torch
A beacon, shining bright in the night
Watching ships sail past
Curved, steep steps taking you to the golden yellow bulb
The sound of crashing waves nearby
People laughing, playing, talking far below
A saviour for ships and their cargo.

So many things this candy cane torch has seen
Once surrounded by sea
Now surrounded by you and me.

Laura Knight
Age 10

Smeaton's Tower

Light house
Massive, bright
Glowing, towering, amazing
A tower that lights up the sea at night
Ship saver

Keira Goodwin
Age 9

Artwork by Chloe Armstrong

Smeaton's Tower

John Smeaton was a Yorkshire man
To design this tower was his light-up plan.

Lit by 24 candles, built using stone and blocks
Made slightly curved, but couldn't stay on the rocks.

The lighting replaced with lenses, it shone
So bright, it stood tall, 22 metres in height.

Getting battered by the sea
Moving the tower
It just had to be.

The tower, rebuilt on a new granite floor
Opened on Plymouth Hoe in September
1884.

Ellia Beeson
Age 8

My Plymouth Journey begins at Smeaton's Tower

A welcoming beam of light
Black clouds mushrooming above the tall lighthouse
The foaming sea that once crashed against the tower
The lighthouse stands tall and proud, saving lives at sea
The mighty journey up all those steps is rewarded with piercing views of Plymouth
The wind races round and round the top of the red-ringed tower.

Archie Cooper
Age 10

Artwork by Ellia Beeson

NEW ST

New Street is in the Barbican area of Plymouth. It was new in 1584, when it was built by prosperous merchants, who made plenty of money in overseas trading. It is now one of the oldest streets in the city.

Widey Court Primary School
Stoke Damerel Community College
Cathedral School of St Mary
Tor Bridge High School
St Peter's Church of England Primary School
Plympton St Maurice Primary School
St Andrew's Church of England Primary School
Manadon Vale Primary School
Laira Green Primary School
Devonport High School for Girls
Oakwood Primary Academy
Woodford Primary Academy
Goosewell Primary Academy
Plymouth Community Intermediate School, MA
West Elementary School, MA
Federal Furnace School, MA
Plymouth South Middle School, MA
Plymouth South High School, MA

UPP
University of Plymouth Press